planning pages®

SCHOOL PLANNER

ACADEMIC & EXTRACURRICULAR

KAHOOTIE CO®

www.kahootie.com

Sunday	Monday	Tuesday	Wednesday

Thursday	Friday	Saturday

Sunday	Monday	Tuesday	Wednesday

Thursday	Friday	Saturday	

Sunday	Monday	Tuesday	Wednesday

Thursday	Friday	Saturday	
			_____
			_____
			_____
			_____
			_____
			_____
			_____
			_____
			_____
			_____
			_____
			_____
			_____
			_____
			_____
			_____
			_____
			_____
			_____
			_____
			_____
			_____
			_____
			_____
			_____
			_____

Sunday	Monday	Tuesday	Wednesday

Thursday	Friday	Saturday	

KAHOOTIE CO.

Sunday	Monday	Tuesday	Wednesday

Thursday	Friday	Saturday	

Sunday	Monday	Tuesday	Wednesday

Thursday	Friday	Saturday

KAHOOTIE CO.

Sunday	Monday	Tuesday	Wednesday

Thursday	Friday	Saturday

Sunday	Monday	Tuesday	Wednesday

Thursday	Friday	Saturday	

Sunday	Monday	Tuesday	Wednesday

KAHOOTIE CO.

Sunday	Monday	Tuesday	Wednesday

Thursday	Friday	Saturday	

Sunday	Monday	Tuesday	Wednesday

Thursday	Friday	Saturday	

Sunday	Monday	Tuesday	Wednesday

Thursday	Friday	Saturday	

Monday /
 School

_____ : _____   _____

_____ : _____   _____

_____ : _____   _____

_____ : _____   _____

_____ : _____

Tuesday /

_____ : _____   _____

_____ : _____   _____

_____ : _____   _____

_____ : _____   _____

_____ : _____   _____

Wednesday /

_____ : _____   _____

_____ : _____   _____

_____ : _____   _____

_____ : _____   _____

_____ : _____   _____

Thursday /

_____ : _____   _____

_____ : _____   _____

_____ : _____   _____

_____ : _____   _____

_____ : _____   _____

Friday /

_____ : _____   _____

_____ : _____   _____

_____ : _____   _____

_____ : _____   _____

_____ : _____   _____

After-School

_____
_____
_____
_____
_____
_____
_____
_____
_____
_____
_____
_____
_____
_____
_____
_____
_____
_____
_____
_____
_____
_____
_____
_____

Weekly Goals :

_____
_____
_____

Chores / Daily To-Do's :

	M	T	W	TH	F	S	S
_____	○	○	○	○	○	○	○
_____	○	○	○	○	○	○	○
_____	○	○	○	○	○	○	○
_____	○	○	○	○	○	○	○
_____	○	○	○	○	○	○	○

Notes :

Weekend Plans

Saturday

Sunday

_____ : _____   _____
_____ : _____   _____
_____ : _____   _____
_____ : _____   _____
_____ : _____   _____

Tuesday   /

_____ : _____   _____
_____ : _____   _____
_____ : _____   _____
_____ : _____   _____
_____ : _____   _____

Wednesday   /

_____ : _____   _____
_____ : _____   _____
_____ : _____   _____
_____ : _____   _____
_____ : _____   _____

Thursday   /

_____ : _____   _____
_____ : _____   _____
_____ : _____   _____
_____ : _____   _____
_____ : _____   _____

Friday   /

_____ : _____   _____
_____ : _____   _____
_____ : _____   _____
_____ : _____   _____
_____ : _____   _____

After-School

_____
_____
_____
_____
_____
_____
_____
_____
_____
_____
_____
_____
_____
_____
_____
_____
_____
_____
_____
_____
_____
_____
_____
_____
_____
_____

Weekly Goals :

_____
_____
_____

Chores / Daily To-Do's :

	M	T	W	TH	F	S	S
_____	○	○	○	○	○	○	○
_____	○	○	○	○	○	○	○
_____	○	○	○	○	○	○	○
_____	○	○	○	○	○	○	○
_____	○	○	○	○	○	○	○

Notes :

Weekend Plans

Saturday	Sunday
_____	_____
_____	_____
_____	_____
_____	_____

Monday / School

_____ : _____

_____ : _____

_____ : _____

_____ : _____

_____ : _____

Tuesday /

_____ : _____

_____ : _____

_____ : _____

_____ : _____

_____ : _____

Wednesday /

_____ : _____

_____ : _____

_____ : _____

_____ : _____

_____ : _____

Thursday /

_____ : _____

_____ : _____

_____ : _____

_____ : _____

_____ : _____

Friday /

_____ : _____

_____ : _____

_____ : _____

_____ : _____

_____ : _____

After-School

_____
_____
_____
_____
_____
_____
_____
_____
_____
_____
_____
_____
_____
_____
_____
_____
_____
_____
_____
_____
_____
_____
_____

Weekly Goals :

_____
_____
_____

Chores / Daily To-Do's :

	M	T	W	TH	F	S	S
_____	◯	◯	◯	◯	◯	◯	◯
_____	◯	◯	◯	◯	◯	◯	◯
_____	◯	◯	◯	◯	◯	◯	◯
_____	◯	◯	◯	◯	◯	◯	◯
_____	◯	◯	◯	◯	◯	◯	◯

Notes :

Weekend Plans

Saturday

_____
_____
_____
_____

Sunday

_____
_____
_____
_____

Monday / *School*

_____ : _____

_____ : _____

_____ : _____

_____ : _____

_____ : _____

Tuesday /

_____ : _____

_____ : _____

_____ : _____

_____ : _____

_____ : _____

Wednesday /

_____ : _____

_____ : _____

_____ : _____

_____ : _____

_____ : _____

Thursday /

_____ : _____

_____ : _____

_____ : _____

_____ : _____

_____ : _____

Friday /

_____ : _____

_____ : _____

_____ : _____

_____ : _____

_____ : _____

After-School

_____
_____
_____
_____
_____
_____
_____
_____
_____
_____
_____
_____
_____
_____
_____
_____
_____
_____
_____
_____
_____
_____

Weekly Goals :

_____
_____
_____

Chores / Daily To-Do's :

	M	T	W	TH	F	S	S
_____	○	○	○	○	○	○	○
_____	○	○	○	○	○	○	○
_____	○	○	○	○	○	○	○
_____	○	○	○	○	○	○	○
_____	○	○	○	○	○	○	○

Notes :

Weekend Plans

Saturday

_____
_____
_____
_____
_____

Sunday

_____
_____
_____
_____

KAHOOTIE CO.

Monday   /   School

_____ : _____   _____
_____ : _____   _____
_____ : _____   _____
_____ : _____   _____
_____ : _____   _____

Tuesday   /

_____ : _____   _____
_____ : _____   _____
_____ : _____   _____
_____ : _____   _____
_____ : _____   _____

Wednesday   /

_____ : _____   _____
_____ : _____   _____
_____ : _____   _____
_____ : _____   _____
_____ : _____   _____

Thursday   /

_____ : _____   _____
_____ : _____   _____
_____ : _____   _____
_____ : _____   _____

Friday   /

_____ : _____   _____
_____ : _____   _____
_____ : _____   _____
_____ : _____   _____

After-School

_____
_____
_____
_____
_____
_____
_____
_____
_____
_____
_____
_____
_____
_____
_____
_____
_____
_____
_____
_____
_____
_____
_____
_____
_____
_____
_____

Weekly Goals :
_____
_____
_____

Chores / Daily To-Do's :   M T W TH F S S

_____   ◯ ◯ ◯ ◯ ◯ ◯ ◯

_____   ◯ ◯ ◯ ◯ ◯ ◯ ◯

_____   ◯ ◯ ◯ ◯ ◯ ◯ ◯

_____   ◯ ◯ ◯ ◯ ◯ ◯ ◯

_____   ◯ ◯ ◯ ◯ ◯ ◯ ◯

Notes :

Weekend Plans

Saturday   Sunday
_____   _____
_____   _____
_____   _____
_____   _____
_____   _____

Monday   /   *School*

_____ : _____   _____
_____ : _____   _____
_____ : _____   _____
_____ : _____   _____
_____ : _____   _____

Tuesday   /

_____ : _____   _____
_____ : _____   _____
_____ : _____   _____
_____ : _____   _____

Wednesday   /

_____ : _____   _____
_____ : _____   _____
_____ : _____   _____
_____ : _____   _____

Thursday   /

_____ : _____   _____
_____ : _____   _____
_____ : _____   _____
_____ : _____   _____

Friday   /

_____ : _____   _____
_____ : _____   _____
_____ : _____   _____
_____ : _____   _____

After-School

_____
_____
_____
_____
_____

_____
_____
_____
_____

_____
_____
_____
_____

_____
_____
_____
_____

_____
_____
_____
_____

Weekly Goals :

_____
_____
_____

Chores / Daily To-Do's : M T W TH F S S

_____ ○ ○ ○ ○ ○ ○ ○

_____ ○ ○ ○ ○ ○ ○ ○

_____ ○ ○ ○ ○ ○ ○ ○

_____ ○ ○ ○ ○ ○ ○ ○

_____ ○ ○ ○ ○ ○ ○ ○

Notes :

Weekend Plans

Saturday   Sunday

_____   _____
_____   _____
_____   _____
_____   _____
_____   _____

KAHOOTIE CO.

Monday   /   School

____ : _____   _____

____ : _____   _____

____ : _____   _____

____ : _____   _____

____ : _____

Tuesday   /

____ : _____   _____

____ : _____   _____

____ : _____   _____

____ : _____   _____

____ : _____

Wednesday   /

____ : _____   _____

____ : _____   _____

____ : _____   _____

____ : _____   _____

____ : _____

Thursday   /

____ : _____   _____

____ : _____   _____

____ : _____   _____

____ : _____   _____

____ : _____

Friday   /

____ : _____   _____

____ : _____   _____

____ : _____   _____

____ : _____   _____

____ : _____

After-School

_____
_____
_____
_____
_____
_____
_____
_____
_____
_____
_____
_____
_____
_____
_____
_____
_____
_____
_____
_____
_____
_____
_____
_____

Weekly Goals :

_____
_____
_____

Chores / Daily To-Do's :

	M	T	W	TH	F	S	S
_____	○	○	○	○	○	○	○
_____	○	○	○	○	○	○	○
_____	○	○	○	○	○	○	○
_____	○	○	○	○	○	○	○
_____	○	○	○	○	○	○	○

Notes :

Weekend Plans

Saturday	Sunday
_____	_____
_____	_____
_____	_____
_____	_____

KAHOOTIE CO.

Monday / School

_____ : _____
_____ : _____
_____ : _____
_____ : _____
_____ : _____

Tuesday /

_____ : _____
_____ : _____
_____ : _____
_____ : _____

Wednesday /

_____ : _____
_____ : _____
_____ : _____
_____ : _____

Thursday /

_____ : _____
_____ : _____
_____ : _____
_____ : _____

Friday /

_____ : _____
_____ : _____
_____ : _____
_____ : _____

After-School

Weekly Goals :

Chores / Daily To-Do's :

	M	T	W	TH	F	S	S
	○	○	○	○	○	○	○
	○	○	○	○	○	○	○
	○	○	○	○	○	○	○
	○	○	○	○	○	○	○
	○	○	○	○	○	○	○

Notes :

Weekend Plans

Saturday

Sunday

Monday   /   *School*

___:_____   _____
___:_____   _____
___:_____   _____
___:_____   _____
___:_____   _____

Tuesday   /

___:_____   _____
___:_____   _____
___:_____   _____
___:_____   _____
___:_____   _____

Wednesday   /

___:_____   _____
___:_____   _____
___:_____   _____
___:_____   _____
___:_____   _____

Thursday   /

___:_____   _____
___:_____   _____
___:_____   _____
___:_____   _____
___:_____   _____

Friday   /

___:_____   _____
___:_____   _____
___:_____   _____
___:_____   _____
___:_____   _____

After-School

Weekly Goals :

Chores / Daily To-Do's :

	M	T	W	TH	F	S	S
	○	○	○	○	○	○	○
	○	○	○	○	○	○	○
	○	○	○	○	○	○	○
	○	○	○	○	○	○	○
	○	○	○	○	○	○	○

Notes :

Weekend Plans

Saturday

Sunday

_____ : _____   _____

_____ : _____   _____

_____ : _____   _____

_____ : _____   _____

_____ : _____   _____

Tuesday   /

_____ : _____   _____

_____ : _____   _____

_____ : _____   _____

_____ : _____   _____

Wednesday   /

_____ : _____   _____

_____ : _____   _____

_____ : _____   _____

_____ : _____   _____

Thursday   /

_____ : _____   _____

_____ : _____   _____

_____ : _____   _____

_____ : _____   _____

Friday   /

_____ : _____   _____

_____ : _____   _____

_____ : _____   _____

_____ : _____   _____

After-School

_____
_____
_____
_____
_____
_____
_____
_____
_____
_____
_____
_____
_____
_____
_____
_____
_____
_____
_____
_____
_____
_____
_____
_____
_____
_____

Weekly Goals :

_____
_____
_____

Chores / Daily To-Do's :

	M	T	W	TH	F	S	S
_____	○	○	○	○	○	○	○
_____	○	○	○	○	○	○	○
_____	○	○	○	○	○	○	○
_____	○	○	○	○	○	○	○
_____	○	○	○	○	○	○	○

Notes :

Weekend Plans

Saturday	Sunday
_____	_____
_____	_____
_____	_____
_____	_____

KAHOOTIE CO.

Monday / School

_____ : _____ _____
_____ : _____ _____
_____ : _____ _____
_____ : _____ _____
_____ : _____ _____

Tuesday /

_____ : _____ _____
_____ : _____ _____
_____ : _____ _____
_____ : _____ _____
_____ : _____ _____

Wednesday /

_____ : _____ _____
_____ : _____ _____
_____ : _____ _____
_____ : _____ _____
_____ : _____ _____

Thursday /

_____ : _____ _____
_____ : _____ _____
_____ : _____ _____
_____ : _____ _____
_____ : _____ _____

Friday /

_____ : _____ _____
_____ : _____ _____
_____ : _____ _____
_____ : _____ _____
_____ : _____ _____

After-School

_____
_____
_____
_____
_____
_____
_____
_____
_____
_____
_____
_____
_____
_____
_____
_____
_____
_____
_____
_____
_____

Weekly Goals :

_____
_____
_____

Chores / Daily To-Do's :

	M	T	W	TH	F	S	S
_____	○	○	○	○	○	○	○
_____	○	○	○	○	○	○	○
_____	○	○	○	○	○	○	○
_____	○	○	○	○	○	○	○
_____	○	○	○	○	○	○	○

Notes :

Weekend Plans

Saturday	Sunday
_____	_____
_____	_____
_____	_____
_____	_____

Monday   /   School

____ : _____   _____
____ : _____   _____
____ : _____   _____
____ : _____   _____
____ : _____   _____

Tuesday   /

____ : _____   _____
____ : _____   _____
____ : _____   _____
____ : _____   _____
____ : _____   _____

Wednesday   /

____ : _____   _____
____ : _____   _____
____ : _____   _____
____ : _____   _____
____ : _____   _____

Thursday   /

____ : _____   _____
____ : _____   _____
____ : _____   _____
____ : _____   _____
____ : _____   _____

Friday   /

____ : _____   _____
____ : _____   _____
____ : _____   _____
____ : _____   _____
____ : _____   _____

After-School

_____
_____
_____
_____
_____
_____
_____
_____
_____
_____
_____
_____
_____
_____
_____
_____
_____
_____
_____
_____
_____
_____
_____
_____

Weekly Goals :

_____
_____
_____

Chores / Daily To-Do's :

	M	T	W	TH	F	S	S
_____	◯	◯	◯	◯	◯	◯	◯
_____	◯	◯	◯	◯	◯	◯	◯
_____	◯	◯	◯	◯	◯	◯	◯
_____	◯	◯	◯	◯	◯	◯	◯
_____	◯	◯	◯	◯	◯	◯	◯

Notes :

Weekend Plans

Saturday	Sunday
_____	_____
_____	_____
_____	_____
_____	_____

Monday / School

___ : _____

___ : _____

___ : _____

___ : _____

___ : _____

Tuesday /

___ : _____

___ : _____

___ : _____

___ : _____

___ : _____

Wednesday /

___ : _____

___ : _____

___ : _____

___ : _____

___ : _____

Thursday /

___ : _____

___ : _____

___ : _____

___ : _____

___ : _____

Friday /

___ : _____

___ : _____

___ : _____

___ : _____

___ : _____

After-School

_____
_____
_____
_____
_____

_____
_____
_____
_____
_____

_____
_____
_____
_____
_____

_____
_____
_____
_____

_____
_____
_____
_____

Weekly Goals :

_____
_____
_____

Chores / Daily To-Do's :

	M	T	W	TH	F	S	S
_____	○	○	○	○	○	○	○
_____	○	○	○	○	○	○	○
_____	○	○	○	○	○	○	○
_____	○	○	○	○	○	○	○
_____	○	○	○	○	○	○	○

Notes :

Weekend Plans

Saturday	Sunday
_____	_____
_____	_____
_____	_____
_____	_____

Monday   /   School

_____ : _____

_____ : _____

_____ : _____

_____ : _____

_____ : _____

Tuesday   /

_____ : _____

_____ : _____

_____ : _____

_____ : _____

_____ : _____

Wednesday   /

_____ : _____

_____ : _____

_____ : _____

_____ : _____

_____ : _____

Thursday   /

_____ : _____

_____ : _____

_____ : _____

_____ : _____

_____ : _____

Friday   /

_____ : _____

_____ : _____

_____ : _____

_____ : _____

_____ : _____

After-School

_____
_____
_____
_____
_____

_____
_____
_____
_____

_____
_____
_____
_____
_____

_____
_____
_____
_____
_____
_____
_____

Weekly Goals :

_____
_____
_____

Chores / Daily To-Do's :

	M	T	W	TH	F	S	S
_____	○	○	○	○	○	○	○
_____	○	○	○	○	○	○	○
_____	○	○	○	○	○	○	○
_____	○	○	○	○	○	○	○
_____	○	○	○	○	○	○	○

Notes :

Weekend Plans

Saturday

_____
_____
_____
_____

Sunday

_____
_____
_____
_____

KAHOOTIE CO.

Monday   /   School

_____ : _____   _____

_____ : _____   _____

_____ : _____   _____

_____ : _____   _____

_____ : _____

Tuesday   /

_____ : _____   _____

_____ : _____   _____

_____ : _____   _____

_____ : _____   _____

_____ : _____   _____

Wednesday   /

_____ : _____   _____

_____ : _____   _____

_____ : _____   _____

_____ : _____   _____

_____ : _____   _____

Thursday   /

_____ : _____   _____

_____ : _____   _____

_____ : _____   _____

_____ : _____   _____

_____ : _____   _____

Friday   /

_____ : _____   _____

_____ : _____   _____

_____ : _____   _____

_____ : _____   _____

_____ : _____   _____

After-School

_____
_____
_____
_____
_____
_____
_____
_____
_____
_____
_____
_____
_____
_____
_____
_____
_____
_____
_____
_____
_____
_____
_____
_____

Weekly Goals :

_____
_____
_____

Chores / Daily To-Do's :

	M	T	W	TH	F	S	S
_____	○	○	○	○	○	○	○
_____	○	○	○	○	○	○	○
_____	○	○	○	○	○	○	○
_____	○	○	○	○	○	○	○
_____	○	○	○	○	○	○	○

Notes :

Weekend Plans

Saturday	Sunday
_____	_____
_____	_____
_____	_____
_____	_____

KAHOOTIE CO.

Monday   /   *School*

_____ : _____   _____
_____ : _____   _____
_____ : _____   _____
_____ : _____   _____
_____ : _____   _____

Tuesday   /

_____ : _____   _____
_____ : _____   _____
_____ : _____   _____
_____ : _____   _____
_____ : _____   _____

Wednesday   /

_____ : _____   _____
_____ : _____   _____
_____ : _____   _____
_____ : _____   _____
_____ : _____   _____

Thursday   /

_____ : _____   _____
_____ : _____   _____
_____ : _____   _____
_____ : _____   _____
_____ : _____   _____

Friday   /

_____ : _____   _____
_____ : _____   _____
_____ : _____   _____
_____ : _____   _____

After-School

Weekly Goals :

Chores / Daily To-Do's :

	M	T	W	TH	F	S	S
	○	○	○	○	○	○	○
	○	○	○	○	○	○	○
	○	○	○	○	○	○	○
	○	○	○	○	○	○	○
	○	○	○	○	○	○	○

Notes :

Weekend Plans

Saturday

Sunday

Monday / School

____ : _____ _____

____ : _____ _____

____ : _____ _____

____ : _____ _____

____ : _____ _____

Tuesday /

____ : _____ _____

____ : _____ _____

____ : _____ _____

____ : _____ _____

____ : _____ _____

Wednesday /

____ : _____ _____

____ : _____ _____

____ : _____ _____

____ : _____ _____

____ : _____ _____

Thursday /

____ : _____ _____

____ : _____ _____

____ : _____ _____

____ : _____ _____

____ : _____ _____

Friday /

____ : _____ _____

____ : _____ _____

____ : _____ _____

____ : _____ _____

____ : _____ _____

After-School

_____
_____
_____
_____
_____
_____
_____
_____
_____
_____
_____
_____
_____
_____
_____
_____
_____
_____
_____

Weekly Goals :

_____
_____
_____

Chores / Daily To-Do's :

	M	T	W	TH	F	S	S
_____	○	○	○	○	○	○	○
_____	○	○	○	○	○	○	○
_____	○	○	○	○	○	○	○
_____	○	○	○	○	○	○	○
	○	○	○	○	○	○	○

Notes :

Weekend Plans

Saturday	Sunday
_____	_____
_____	_____
_____	_____
_____	_____

Monday /

_____ : _____ _____

_____ : _____ _____

_____ : _____ _____

_____ : _____ _____

_____ : _____ _____

Tuesday /

_____ : _____ _____

_____ : _____ _____

_____ : _____ _____

_____ : _____ _____

_____ : _____ _____

Wednesday /

_____ : _____ _____

_____ : _____ _____

_____ : _____ _____

_____ : _____ _____

_____ : _____ _____

Thursday /

_____ : _____ _____

_____ : _____ _____

_____ : _____ _____

_____ : _____ _____

_____ : _____ _____

Friday /

_____ : _____ _____

_____ : _____ _____

_____ : _____ _____

_____ : _____ _____

_____ : _____ _____

After-School

_____
_____
_____
_____
_____
_____
_____
_____
_____
_____
_____
_____
_____
_____
_____
_____
_____
_____
_____
_____
_____
_____
_____

Weekly Goals :

_____
_____
_____

Chores / Daily To-Do's :

	M	T	W	TH	F	S	S
_____	◯	◯	◯	◯	◯	◯	◯
_____	◯	◯	◯	◯	◯	◯	◯
_____	◯	◯	◯	◯	◯	◯	◯
_____	◯	◯	◯	◯	◯	◯	◯
_____	◯	◯	◯	◯	◯	◯	◯

Notes :

Weekend Plans

Saturday

_____
_____
_____
_____

Sunday

_____
_____
_____
_____

KAHOOTIE CO.

Monday   /   School

___ : _____   _____

___ : _____   _____

___ : _____   _____

___ : _____   _____

___ : _____   _____

Tuesday   /

___ : _____   _____

___ : _____   _____

___ : _____   _____

___ : _____   _____

___ : _____   _____

Wednesday   /

___ : _____   _____

___ : _____   _____

___ : _____   _____

___ : _____   _____

___ : _____   _____

Thursday   /

___ : _____   _____

___ : _____   _____

___ : _____   _____

___ : _____   _____

___ : _____   _____

Friday   /

___ : _____   _____

___ : _____   _____

___ : _____   _____

___ : _____   _____

___ : _____   _____

After-School

_____
_____
_____
_____
_____
_____
_____
_____
_____
_____
_____
_____
_____
_____
_____
_____
_____
_____
_____
_____
_____
_____
_____

Weekly Goals :

_____
_____
_____

Chores / Daily To-Do's :

	M	T	W	TH	F	S	S
_____	○	○	○	○	○	○	○
_____	○	○	○	○	○	○	○
_____	○	○	○	○	○	○	○
_____	○	○	○	○	○	○	○
	○	○	○	○	○	○	○

Notes :

Weekend Plans

Saturday	Sunday
_____	_____
_____	_____
_____	_____
_____	_____

Monday   /   School

_____ : _____   _____
_____ : _____   _____
_____ : _____   _____
_____ : _____   _____
_____ : _____   _____

Tuesday   /

_____ : _____   _____
_____ : _____   _____
_____ : _____   _____
_____ : _____   _____
_____ : _____   _____

Wednesday   /

_____ : _____   _____
_____ : _____   _____
_____ : _____   _____
_____ : _____   _____

Thursday   /

_____ : _____   _____
_____ : _____   _____
_____ : _____   _____
_____ : _____   _____

Friday   /

_____ : _____   _____
_____ : _____   _____
_____ : _____   _____
_____ : _____   _____

After-School

_____
_____
_____
_____
_____
_____
_____
_____
_____
_____
_____
_____
_____
_____
_____
_____
_____
_____
_____
_____
_____
_____
_____

Weekly Goals :

_____
_____
_____

Chores / Daily To-Do's :   M T W TH F S S

_____   ○ ○ ○ ○ ○ ○ ○

_____   ○ ○ ○ ○ ○ ○ ○

_____   ○ ○ ○ ○ ○ ○ ○

_____   ○ ○ ○ ○ ○ ○ ○

_____   ○ ○ ○ ○ ○ ○ ○

Notes :

Weekend Plans

Saturday   Sunday

_____   _____
_____   _____
_____   _____
_____   _____
_____   _____

Monday / School

____ : _____

____ : _____

____ : _____

____ : _____

____ : _____

Tuesday /

____ : _____

____ : _____

____ : _____

____ : _____

____ : _____

Wednesday /

____ : _____

____ : _____

____ : _____

____ : _____

____ : _____

Thursday /

____ : _____

____ : _____

____ : _____

____ : _____

____ : _____

Friday /

____ : _____

____ : _____

____ : _____

____ : _____

____ : _____

After-School

_____
_____
_____
_____
_____
_____
_____
_____
_____
_____
_____
_____
_____
_____
_____
_____
_____
_____
_____
_____
_____
_____
_____

Weekly Goals :

_____
_____
_____

Chores / Daily To-Do's : M T W TH F S S

_____ ○ ○ ○ ○ ○ ○ ○
_____ ○ ○ ○ ○ ○ ○ ○
_____ ○ ○ ○ ○ ○ ○ ○
_____ ○ ○ ○ ○ ○ ○ ○
_____ ○ ○ ○ ○ ○ ○ ○

Notes :

Weekend Plans

Saturday	Sunday
_____	_____
_____	_____
_____	_____
_____	_____

Monday / School

_____ : _____

_____ : _____

_____ : _____

_____ : _____

_____ : _____

Tuesday /

_____ : _____

_____ : _____

_____ : _____

_____ : _____

_____ : _____

Wednesday /

_____ : _____

_____ : _____

_____ : _____

_____ : _____

Thursday /

_____ : _____

_____ : _____

_____ : _____

_____ : _____

Friday /

_____ : _____

_____ : _____

_____ : _____

_____ : _____

_____
_____
_____
_____
_____
_____
_____
_____
_____
_____
_____
_____
_____
_____
_____
_____
_____
_____
_____
_____
_____
_____
_____
_____
_____
_____

Weekly Goals :
_____
_____
_____

Chores / Daily To-Do's :   M T W TH F S S

_____   ○ ○ ○ ○ ○ ○ ○
_____   ○ ○ ○ ○ ○ ○ ○
_____   ○ ○ ○ ○ ○ ○ ○
_____   ○ ○ ○ ○ ○ ○ ○
_____   ○ ○ ○ ○ ○ ○ ○

Notes :

Weekend Plans

Saturday   Sunday
_____   _____
_____   _____
_____   _____
_____   _____

Monday   /   *School*

_____ : _____   _____
_____ : _____   _____
_____ : _____   _____
_____ : _____   _____
_____ : _____   _____

Tuesday   /

_____ : _____   _____
_____ : _____   _____
_____ : _____   _____
_____ : _____   _____
_____ : _____   _____

Wednesday   /

_____ : _____   _____
_____ : _____   _____
_____ : _____   _____
_____ : _____   _____

Thursday   /

_____ : _____   _____
_____ : _____   _____
_____ : _____   _____
_____ : _____   _____

Friday   /

_____ : _____   _____
_____ : _____   _____
_____ : _____   _____
_____ : _____   _____
_____ : _____   _____

After-School

_____
_____
_____
_____
_____
_____
_____
_____
_____
_____
_____
_____
_____
_____
_____
_____
_____
_____
_____
_____
_____
_____
_____

Weekly Goals :

_____
_____
_____

Chores / Daily To-Do's :   M T W TH F S S

_____   ◯ ◯ ◯ ◯ ◯ ◯ ◯

_____   ◯ ◯ ◯ ◯ ◯ ◯ ◯

_____   ◯ ◯ ◯ ◯ ◯ ◯ ◯

_____   ◯ ◯ ◯ ◯ ◯ ◯ ◯

_____   ◯ ◯ ◯ ◯ ◯ ◯ ◯

Notes :

Weekend Plans

Saturday   Sunday

_____   _____
_____   _____
_____   _____
_____   _____

Monday   /   *School*

_____ : _____   _____
_____ : _____   _____
_____ : _____   _____
_____ : _____   _____
_____ : _____   _____

Tuesday   /

_____ : _____   _____
_____ : _____   _____
_____ : _____   _____
_____ : _____   _____
_____ : _____   _____

Wednesday   /

_____ : _____   _____
_____ : _____   _____
_____ : _____   _____
_____ : _____   _____
_____ : _____   _____

Thursday   /

_____ : _____   _____
_____ : _____   _____
_____ : _____   _____
_____ : _____   _____
_____ : _____   _____

Friday   /

_____ : _____   _____
_____ : _____   _____
_____ : _____   _____
_____ : _____   _____
_____ : _____   _____

After-School

_____
_____
_____
_____
_____

_____
_____
_____
_____
_____

_____
_____
_____
_____
_____

_____
_____
_____
_____
_____

_____
_____
_____
_____

Weekly Goals :

_____
_____
_____

Chores / Daily To-Do's :

	M	T	W	TH	F	S	S
_____	○	○	○	○	○	○	○
_____	○	○	○	○	○	○	○
_____	○	○	○	○	○	○	○
_____	○	○	○	○	○	○	○
_____	○	○	○	○	○	○	○

Notes :

Weekend Plans

Saturday	Sunday
_____	_____
_____	_____
_____	_____
_____	_____

_____ : _____   _____

_____ : _____   _____

_____ : _____   _____

_____ : _____   _____

_____ : _____   _____

Tuesday   /

_____ : _____   _____

_____ : _____   _____

_____ : _____   _____

_____ : _____   _____

_____ : _____   _____

Wednesday   /

_____ : _____   _____

_____ : _____   _____

_____ : _____   _____

_____ : _____   _____

_____ : _____   _____

Thursday   /

_____ : _____   _____

_____ : _____   _____

_____ : _____   _____

_____ : _____   _____

_____ : _____   _____

Friday   /

_____ : _____   _____

_____ : _____   _____

_____ : _____   _____

_____ : _____   _____

_____ : _____   _____

After-School

_____
_____
_____
_____
_____
_____
_____
_____
_____
_____
_____
_____
_____
_____
_____
_____
_____
_____
_____
_____
_____
_____
_____
_____
_____

Weekly Goals :

_____
_____
_____

Chores / Daily To-Do's :   M T W TH F S S

_____   ◯ ◯ ◯ ◯ ◯ ◯ ◯
_____   ◯ ◯ ◯ ◯ ◯ ◯ ◯
_____   ◯ ◯ ◯ ◯ ◯ ◯ ◯
_____   ◯ ◯ ◯ ◯ ◯ ◯ ◯
_____   ◯ ◯ ◯ ◯ ◯ ◯ ◯

Notes :

Weekend Plans

Saturday	Sunday
_____	_____
_____	_____
_____	_____
_____	_____
_____	_____

Monday   /   School

_____ : _____   _____
_____ : _____   _____
_____ : _____   _____
_____ : _____   _____
_____ : _____   _____

Tuesday   /

_____ : _____   _____
_____ : _____   _____
_____ : _____   _____
_____ : _____   _____
_____ : _____   _____

Wednesday   /

_____ : _____   _____
_____ : _____   _____
_____ : _____   _____
_____ : _____   _____
_____ : _____   _____

Thursday   /

_____ : _____   _____
_____ : _____   _____
_____ : _____   _____
_____ : _____   _____

Friday   /

_____ : _____   _____
_____ : _____   _____
_____ : _____   _____
_____ : _____   _____

After-School

Weekly Goals :

_____
_____
_____

Chores / Daily To-Do's :   M T W TH F S S

_____ ◯ ◯ ◯ ◯ ◯ ◯ ◯

_____ ◯ ◯ ◯ ◯ ◯ ◯ ◯

_____ ◯ ◯ ◯ ◯ ◯ ◯ ◯

_____ ◯ ◯ ◯ ◯ ◯ ◯ ◯

_____ ◯ ◯ ◯ ◯ ◯ ◯ ◯

Notes :

Weekend Plans

Saturday   Sunday

_____   _____
_____   _____
_____   _____
_____   _____
_____   _____

Monday / *School*

_____ : _____
_____ : _____
_____ : _____
_____ : _____
_____ : _____

Tuesday /

_____ : _____
_____ : _____
_____ : _____
_____ : _____
_____ : _____

Wednesday /

_____ : _____
_____ : _____
_____ : _____
_____ : _____
_____ : _____

Thursday /

_____ : _____
_____ : _____
_____ : _____
_____ : _____
_____ : _____

Friday /

_____ : _____
_____ : _____
_____ : _____
_____ : _____
_____ : _____

After-School

_____
_____
_____
_____
_____
_____
_____
_____
_____
_____
_____
_____
_____
_____
_____
_____
_____
_____
_____
_____
_____
_____
_____
_____
_____
_____
_____
_____

Weekly Goals :

_____
_____
_____

Chores / Daily To-Do's :   M T W TH F S S

_____   ◯ ◯ ◯ ◯ ◯ ◯ ◯

_____   ◯ ◯ ◯ ◯ ◯ ◯ ◯

_____   ◯ ◯ ◯ ◯ ◯ ◯ ◯

_____   ◯ ◯ ◯ ◯ ◯ ◯ ◯

_____   ◯ ◯ ◯ ◯ ◯ ◯ ◯

Notes :

Weekend Plans

Saturday   Sunday

_____   _____
_____   _____
_____   _____
_____   _____

Monday / School

____ : _____ _____

____ : _____ _____

____ : _____ _____

____ : _____ _____

____ : _____ _____

Tuesday /

____ : _____ _____

____ : _____ _____

____ : _____ _____

____ : _____ _____

____ : _____ _____

Wednesday /

____ : _____ _____

____ : _____ _____

____ : _____ _____

____ : _____ _____

____ : _____ _____

Thursday /

____ : _____ _____

____ : _____ _____

____ : _____ _____

____ : _____ _____

____ : _____ _____

Friday /

____ : _____ _____

____ : _____ _____

____ : _____ _____

____ : _____ _____

____ : _____ _____

After-School

_____
_____
_____
_____
_____

_____
_____
_____
_____
_____

_____
_____
_____
_____
_____
_____
_____
_____
_____
_____
_____
_____
_____
_____
_____

Weekly Goals :

_____
_____
_____

Chores / Daily To-Do's :   M T W TH F S S

_____   ◯ ◯ ◯ ◯ ◯ ◯ ◯
_____   ◯ ◯ ◯ ◯ ◯ ◯ ◯
_____   ◯ ◯ ◯ ◯ ◯ ◯ ◯
_____   ◯ ◯ ◯ ◯ ◯ ◯ ◯
_____   ◯ ◯ ◯ ◯ ◯ ◯ ◯

Notes :

Weekend Plans

Saturday   Sunday

_____   _____
_____   _____
_____   _____
_____   _____

KAHOOTIE CO.

Monday / School

_____ : _____ _____
_____ : _____ _____
_____ : _____ _____
_____ : _____ _____
_____ : _____ _____

Tuesday /

_____ : _____ _____
_____ : _____ _____
_____ : _____ _____
_____ : _____ _____
_____ : _____ _____

Wednesday /

_____ : _____ _____
_____ : _____ _____
_____ : _____ _____
_____ : _____ _____
_____ : _____ _____

Thursday /

_____ : _____ _____
_____ : _____ _____
_____ : _____ _____
_____ : _____ _____
_____ : _____ _____

Friday /

_____ : _____ _____
_____ : _____ _____
_____ : _____ _____
_____ : _____ _____
_____ : _____ _____

After-School

_____
_____
_____
_____
_____
_____
_____
_____
_____
_____
_____
_____
_____
_____
_____
_____
_____
_____
_____
_____
_____
_____
_____
_____
_____

Weekly Goals :

_____
_____
_____

Chores / Daily To-Do's :

	M	T	W	TH	F	S	S
_____	○	○	○	○	○	○	○
_____	○	○	○	○	○	○	○
_____	○	○	○	○	○	○	○
_____	○	○	○	○	○	○	○
_____	○	○	○	○	○	○	○

Notes :

Weekend Plans

Saturday	Sunday
_____	_____
_____	_____
_____	_____
_____	_____
_____	_____

Monday / School

_____ : _____

_____ : _____

_____ : _____

_____ : _____

_____ : _____

Tuesday /

_____ : _____

_____ : _____

_____ : _____

_____ : _____

_____ : _____

Wednesday /

_____ : _____

_____ : _____

_____ : _____

_____ : _____

_____ : _____

Thursday /

_____ : _____

_____ : _____

_____ : _____

_____ : _____

Friday /

_____ : _____

_____ : _____

_____ : _____

_____ : _____

_____ : _____

After-School

_____
_____
_____
_____
_____
_____
_____
_____
_____
_____
_____

_____
_____
_____
_____
_____

_____
_____
_____
_____

Weekly Goals :

_____
_____
_____

Chores / Daily To-Do's :

M T W TH F S S

_____ ○ ○ ○ ○ ○ ○ ○
_____ ○ ○ ○ ○ ○ ○ ○
_____ ○ ○ ○ ○ ○ ○ ○
_____ ○ ○ ○ ○ ○ ○ ○
_____ ○ ○ ○ ○ ○ ○ ○

Notes :

Weekend Plans

Saturday   Sunday

_____   _____
_____   _____
_____   _____
_____   _____
_____   _____

KAHOOTIE CO.

Monday   /   School

____ : _____   _____
____ : _____   _____
____ : _____   _____
____ : _____   _____
____ : _____   _____

Tuesday   /

____ : _____   _____
____ : _____   _____
____ : _____   _____
____ : _____   _____
____ : _____   _____

Wednesday   /

____ : _____   _____
____ : _____   _____
____ : _____   _____
____ : _____   _____
____ : _____   _____

Thursday   /

____ : _____   _____
____ : _____   _____
____ : _____   _____
____ : _____   _____
____ : _____   _____

Friday   /

____ : _____   _____
____ : _____   _____
____ : _____   _____
____ : _____   _____
____ : _____   _____

After-School

_____
_____
_____
_____
_____
_____
_____
_____
_____
_____
_____
_____
_____
_____
_____
_____
_____
_____
_____
_____
_____
_____
_____

Weekly Goals :

_____
_____
_____

Chores / Daily To-Do's :

	M	T	W	TH	F	S	S
_____	○	○	○	○	○	○	○
_____	○	○	○	○	○	○	○
_____	○	○	○	○	○	○	○
_____	○	○	○	○	○	○	○
_____	○	○	○	○	○	○	○

Notes :

Weekend Plans

Saturday	Sunday
_____	_____
_____	_____
_____	_____
_____	_____
_____	_____

Monday /   *School*

____ : _____   _____

____ : _____   _____

____ : _____   _____

____ : _____   _____

____ : _____   _____

Tuesday /

____ : _____   _____

____ : _____   _____

____ : _____   _____

____ : _____   _____

____ : _____   _____

Wednesday /

____ : _____   _____

____ : _____   _____

____ : _____   _____

____ : _____   _____

____ : _____   _____

Thursday /

____ : _____   _____

____ : _____   _____

____ : _____   _____

____ : _____   _____

____ : _____   _____

Friday /

____ : _____   _____

____ : _____   _____

____ : _____   _____

____ : _____   _____

____ : _____   _____

After-School

_____
_____
_____
_____
_____

_____
_____
_____
_____
_____

_____
_____
_____
_____
_____

_____
_____
_____
_____
_____

_____
_____
_____
_____
_____

Weekly Goals :

_____
_____
_____

Chores / Daily To-Do's : M T W TH F S S

_____ ◯ ◯ ◯ ◯ ◯ ◯ ◯

_____ ◯ ◯ ◯ ◯ ◯ ◯ ◯

_____ ◯ ◯ ◯ ◯ ◯ ◯ ◯

_____ ◯ ◯ ◯ ◯ ◯ ◯ ◯

_____ ◯ ◯ ◯ ◯ ◯ ◯ ◯

Notes :

Weekend Plans

Saturday   Sunday

_____   _____
_____   _____
_____   _____
_____   _____
_____   _____

Monday   /   *School*

_____ : _____   _____
_____ : _____   _____
_____ : _____   _____
_____ : _____   _____
_____ : _____   _____

Tuesday   /

_____ : _____   _____
_____ : _____   _____
_____ : _____   _____
_____ : _____   _____
_____ : _____   _____

Wednesday   /

_____ : _____   _____
_____ : _____   _____
_____ : _____   _____
_____ : _____   _____
_____ : _____   _____

Thursday   /

_____ : _____   _____
_____ : _____   _____
_____ : _____   _____
_____ : _____   _____
_____ : _____   _____

Friday   /

_____ : _____   _____
_____ : _____   _____
_____ : _____   _____
_____ : _____   _____
_____ : _____   _____

After-School

_____
_____
_____
_____
_____
_____
_____
_____
_____
_____
_____
_____
_____
_____
_____
_____
_____
_____
_____
_____
_____
_____
_____
_____

Weekly Goals :

_____
_____
_____

Chores / Daily To-Do's :

	M	T	W	TH	F	S	S
_____	○	○	○	○	○	○	○
_____	○	○	○	○	○	○	○
_____	○	○	○	○	○	○	○
_____	○	○	○	○	○	○	○
_____	○	○	○	○	○	○	○

Notes :

Weekend Plans

Saturday

_____
_____
_____
_____
_____

Sunday

_____
_____
_____
_____
_____

Monday   /   School

_____ : _____   _____
_____ : _____   _____
_____ : _____   _____
_____ : _____   _____
_____ : _____   _____

Tuesday   /

_____ : _____   _____
_____ : _____   _____
_____ : _____   _____
_____ : _____   _____
_____ : _____   _____

Wednesday   /

_____ : _____   _____
_____ : _____   _____
_____ : _____   _____
_____ : _____   _____
_____ : _____   _____

Thursday   /

_____ : _____   _____
_____ : _____   _____
_____ : _____   _____
_____ : _____   _____

Friday   /

_____ : _____   _____
_____ : _____   _____
_____ : _____   _____
_____ : _____   _____
_____ : _____   _____

After-School

_____
_____
_____
_____
_____
_____
_____
_____
_____
_____
_____
_____
_____
_____
_____
_____
_____
_____
_____
_____
_____
_____
_____

Weekly Goals :

_____
_____
_____

Chores / Daily To-Do's :

	M	T	W	TH	F	S	S
_____	○	○	○	○	○	○	○
_____	○	○	○	○	○	○	○
_____	○	○	○	○	○	○	○
_____	○	○	○	○	○	○	○
_____	○	○	○	○	○	○	○

Notes :

Weekend Plans

Saturday	Sunday
_____	_____
_____	_____
_____	_____
_____	_____
_____	_____

Monday / School

____ : _____   _____
____ : _____   _____
____ : _____   _____
____ : _____   _____
____ : _____   _____

Tuesday /

____ : _____   _____
____ : _____   _____
____ : _____   _____
____ : _____   _____

Wednesday /

____ : _____   _____
____ : _____   _____
____ : _____   _____
____ : _____   _____

Thursday /

____ : _____   _____
____ : _____   _____
____ : _____   _____
____ : _____   _____

Friday /

____ : _____   _____
____ : _____   _____
____ : _____   _____
____ : _____   _____

After-School

_____
_____
_____
_____
_____
_____
_____
_____
_____
_____
_____
_____
_____
_____
_____
_____
_____
_____
_____
_____

Weekly Goals :

_____
_____
_____

Chores / Daily To-Do's :   M T W TH F S S

_____ ◯ ◯ ◯ ◯ ◯ ◯ ◯
_____ ◯ ◯ ◯ ◯ ◯ ◯ ◯
_____ ◯ ◯ ◯ ◯ ◯ ◯ ◯
_____ ◯ ◯ ◯ ◯ ◯ ◯ ◯
_____ ◯ ◯ ◯ ◯ ◯ ◯ ◯

Notes :

Weekend Plans

Saturday	Sunday
_____	_____
_____	_____
_____	_____
_____	_____
_____	_____

Monday	/	School
___ :		
___ :		
___ :		
___ :		
___ :		

Tuesday /

___ :		
___ :		
___ :		
___ :		
___ :		

Wednesday /

___ :		
___ :		
___ :		
___ :		
___ :		

Thursday /

___ :		
___ :		
___ :		
___ :		
___ :		

Friday /

___ :		
___ :		
___ :		
___ :		
___ :		

After-School

Weekly Goals :

Chores / Daily To-Do's :   M T W TH F S S

Notes :

Weekend Plans

Saturday   Sunday

Monday / School

___ : _____
___ : _____
___ : _____
___ : _____
___ : _____

Tuesday /

___ : _____
___ : _____
___ : _____
___ : _____
___ : _____

Wednesday /

___ : _____
___ : _____
___ : _____
___ : _____
___ : _____

Thursday /

___ : _____
___ : _____
___ : _____
___ : _____
___ : _____

Friday /

___ : _____
___ : _____
___ : _____
___ : _____
___ : _____

After-School

_____
_____
_____
_____
_____
_____
_____
_____
_____
_____
_____
_____
_____
_____
_____
_____
_____
_____
_____
_____
_____
_____
_____
_____
_____

Weekly Goals :
_____
_____
_____

Chores / Daily To-Do's :   M T W TH F S S

_____ ◯ ◯ ◯ ◯ ◯ ◯ ◯
_____ ◯ ◯ ◯ ◯ ◯ ◯ ◯
_____ ◯ ◯ ◯ ◯ ◯ ◯ ◯
_____ ◯ ◯ ◯ ◯ ◯ ◯ ◯
_____ ◯ ◯ ◯ ◯ ◯ ◯ ◯

Notes :

Weekend Plans

Saturday   Sunday
_____   _____
_____   _____
_____   _____
_____   _____
_____   _____

Monday   /   *School*

_____ : _____   _____

_____ : _____   _____

_____ : _____   _____

_____ : _____   _____

_____ : _____   _____

Tuesday   /

_____ : _____   _____

_____ : _____   _____

_____ : _____   _____

_____ : _____   _____

_____ : _____   _____

Wednesday   /

_____ : _____   _____

_____ : _____   _____

_____ : _____   _____

_____ : _____   _____

_____ : _____   _____

Thursday   /

_____ : _____   _____

_____ : _____   _____

_____ : _____   _____

_____ : _____   _____

Friday   /

_____ : _____   _____

_____ : _____   _____

_____ : _____   _____

_____ : _____   _____

After-School

Weekly Goals :

Chores / Daily To-Do's :

	M	T	W	TH	F	S	S
	○	○	○	○	○	○	○
	○	○	○	○	○	○	○
	○	○	○	○	○	○	○
	○	○	○	○	○	○	○
	○	○	○	○	○	○	○

Notes :

Weekend Plans

Saturday

Sunday

Monday   /   *School*

_____ : _____   _____
_____ : _____   _____
_____ : _____   _____
_____ : _____   _____
_____ : _____   _____

Tuesday   /

_____ : _____   _____
_____ : _____   _____
_____ : _____   _____
_____ : _____   _____
_____ : _____   _____

Wednesday   /

_____ : _____   _____
_____ : _____   _____
_____ : _____   _____
_____ : _____   _____
_____ : _____   _____

Thursday   /

_____ : _____   _____
_____ : _____   _____
_____ : _____   _____
_____ : _____   _____

Friday   /

_____ : _____   _____
_____ : _____   _____
_____ : _____   _____
_____ : _____   _____
_____ : _____   _____

After-School

_____
_____
_____
_____
_____
_____
_____
_____
_____
_____
_____
_____
_____
_____
_____
_____
_____
_____
_____
_____
_____
_____

Weekly Goals :

_____
_____
_____

Chores / Daily To-Do's : M T W TH F S S

_____ ◯ ◯ ◯ ◯ ◯ ◯ ◯

_____ ◯ ◯ ◯ ◯ ◯ ◯ ◯

_____ ◯ ◯ ◯ ◯ ◯ ◯ ◯

_____ ◯ ◯ ◯ ◯ ◯ ◯ ◯

_____ ◯ ◯ ◯ ◯ ◯ ◯ ◯

Notes :

Weekend Plans

Saturday   Sunday

_____   _____
_____   _____
_____   _____
_____   _____
_____   _____

Monday / School

_____ : _____   _____
_____ : _____   _____
_____ : _____   _____
_____ : _____   _____
_____ : _____   _____

Tuesday /

_____ : _____   _____
_____ : _____   _____
_____ : _____   _____
_____ : _____   _____
_____ : _____   _____

Wednesday /

_____ : _____   _____
_____ : _____   _____
_____ : _____   _____
_____ : _____   _____

Thursday /

_____ : _____   _____
_____ : _____   _____
_____ : _____   _____
_____ : _____   _____

Friday /

_____ : _____   _____
_____ : _____   _____
_____ : _____   _____
_____ : _____   _____

After-School

_____
_____
_____
_____
_____
_____
_____
_____
_____
_____
_____
_____
_____
_____
_____
_____
_____
_____
_____
_____
_____
_____
_____
_____
_____
_____
_____
_____
_____
_____
_____

Weekly Goals :

_____
_____
_____

Chores / Daily To-Do's :   M T W TH F S S

_____   ◯ ◯ ◯ ◯ ◯ ◯ ◯

_____   ◯ ◯ ◯ ◯ ◯ ◯ ◯

_____   ◯ ◯ ◯ ◯ ◯ ◯ ◯

_____   ◯ ◯ ◯ ◯ ◯ ◯ ◯

_____   ◯ ◯ ◯ ◯ ◯ ◯ ◯

Notes :

Weekend Plans

Saturday   Sunday

_____   _____
_____   _____
_____   _____
_____   _____
_____   _____

Monday   /   School

_____ : _____   _____

_____ : _____   _____

_____ : _____   _____

_____ : _____   _____

_____ : _____   _____

Tuesday   /

_____ : _____   _____

_____ : _____   _____

_____ : _____   _____

_____ : _____   _____

_____ : _____   _____

Wednesday   /

_____ : _____   _____

_____ : _____   _____

_____ : _____   _____

_____ : _____   _____

_____ : _____   _____

Thursday   /

_____ : _____   _____

_____ : _____   _____

_____ : _____   _____

_____ : _____   _____

_____ : _____   _____

Friday   /

_____ : _____   _____

_____ : _____   _____

_____ : _____   _____

_____ : _____   _____

_____ : _____   _____

After-School

_____
_____
_____
_____
_____
_____
_____
_____
_____
_____
_____
_____
_____
_____
_____
_____
_____
_____
_____
_____
_____
_____
_____
_____
_____
_____
_____

Weekly Goals :
_____
_____
_____

Chores / Daily To-Do's : M T W TH F S S

_____ ◯ ◯ ◯ ◯ ◯ ◯ ◯

_____ ◯ ◯ ◯ ◯ ◯ ◯ ◯

_____ ◯ ◯ ◯ ◯ ◯ ◯ ◯

_____ ◯ ◯ ◯ ◯ ◯ ◯ ◯

_____ ◯ ◯ ◯ ◯ ◯ ◯ ◯

Notes :

Weekend Plans

Saturday   Sunday
_____   _____
_____   _____
_____   _____
_____   _____
_____   _____

KAHOOTIE CO.

Monday / School

___ : ___
___ : ___
___ : ___
___ : ___
___ : ___

Tuesday /

___ : ___
___ : ___
___ : ___
___ : ___
___ : ___

Wednesday /

___ : ___
___ : ___
___ : ___
___ : ___
___ : ___

Thursday /

___ : ___
___ : ___
___ : ___
___ : ___

Friday /

___ : ___
___ : ___
___ : ___
___ : ___

After-School

_____
_____
_____
_____
_____
_____
_____
_____
_____
_____
_____
_____
_____
_____
_____
_____
_____
_____
_____
_____
_____
_____

Weekly Goals :
_____
_____
_____

Chores / Daily To-Do's :   M T W TH F S S

_____   ◯ ◯ ◯ ◯ ◯ ◯ ◯
_____   ◯ ◯ ◯ ◯ ◯ ◯ ◯
_____   ◯ ◯ ◯ ◯ ◯ ◯ ◯
_____   ◯ ◯ ◯ ◯ ◯ ◯ ◯
_____   ◯ ◯ ◯ ◯ ◯ ◯ ◯

Notes :

Weekend Plans

Saturday   Sunday

_____   _____
_____   _____
_____   _____
_____   _____
_____   _____

Monday   /   *School*

____ : _____   _____
____ : _____   _____
____ : _____   _____
____ : _____   _____
____ : _____   _____

Tuesday   /

____ : _____   _____
____ : _____   _____
____ : _____   _____
____ : _____   _____
____ : _____   _____

Wednesday   /

____ : _____   _____
____ : _____   _____
____ : _____   _____
____ : _____   _____
____ : _____   _____

Thursday   /

____ : _____   _____
____ : _____   _____
____ : _____   _____
____ : _____   _____

Friday   /

____ : _____   _____
____ : _____   _____
____ : _____   _____
____ : _____   _____
____ : _____   _____

After-School

Weekly Goals :

Chores / Daily To-Do's : M T W TH F S S

Notes :

Weekend Plans

Saturday   Sunday

Monday   /   *School*

___ : _____   _____
___ : _____   _____
___ : _____   _____
___ : _____   _____
___ : _____   _____

Tuesday   /

___ : _____   _____
___ : _____   _____
___ : _____   _____
___ : _____   _____
___ : _____   _____

Wednesday   /

___ : _____   _____
___ : _____   _____
___ : _____   _____
___ : _____   _____
___ : _____   _____

Thursday   /

___ : _____   _____
___ : _____   _____
___ : _____   _____
___ : _____   _____

Friday   /

___ : _____   _____
___ : _____   _____
___ : _____   _____
___ : _____   _____

After-School

_____
_____
_____
_____
_____
_____
_____
_____
_____
_____
_____
_____
_____
_____
_____
_____
_____
_____
_____
_____
_____
_____
_____
_____

Weekly Goals :
_____
_____
_____

Chores / Daily To-Do's :   M T W TH F S S

_____   ○ ○ ○ ○ ○ ○ ○

_____   ○ ○ ○ ○ ○ ○ ○

_____   ○ ○ ○ ○ ○ ○ ○

_____   ○ ○ ○ ○ ○ ○ ○

_____   ○ ○ ○ ○ ○ ○ ○

Notes :

───────────────── Weekend Plans ─────────────────

Saturday   Sunday

_____   _____
_____   _____
_____   _____
_____   _____
_____   _____

Monday   /   *School*

_____ : _____

_____ : _____

_____ : _____

_____ : _____

_____ : _____

Tuesday   /

_____ : _____

_____ : _____

_____ : _____

_____ : _____

_____ : _____

Wednesday   /

_____ : _____

_____ : _____

_____ : _____

_____ : _____

_____ : _____

Thursday   /

_____ : _____

_____ : _____

_____ : _____

_____ : _____

_____ : _____

Friday   /

_____ : _____

_____ : _____

_____ : _____

_____ : _____

_____ : _____

After-School

_____
_____
_____
_____
_____
_____
_____
_____
_____
_____
_____
_____
_____
_____
_____
_____
_____
_____
_____
_____
_____
_____
_____

Weekly Goals :

_____
_____
_____

Chores / Daily To-Do's :

	M	T	W	TH	F	S	S
_____	○	○	○	○	○	○	○
_____	○	○	○	○	○	○	○
_____	○	○	○	○	○	○	○
_____	○	○	○	○	○	○	○
_____	○	○	○	○	○	○	○

Notes :

Weekend Plans

Saturday

_____

_____

_____

_____

Sunday

_____

_____

_____

_____

Monday   /   School

_____ : _____   _____
_____ : _____   _____
_____ : _____   _____
_____ : _____   _____
_____ : _____   _____

Tuesday   /

_____ : _____   _____
_____ : _____   _____
_____ : _____   _____
_____ : _____   _____

Wednesday   /

_____ : _____   _____
_____ : _____   _____
_____ : _____   _____
_____ : _____   _____

Thursday   /

_____ : _____   _____
_____ : _____   _____
_____ : _____   _____
_____ : _____   _____

Friday   /

_____ : _____   _____
_____ : _____   _____
_____ : _____   _____
_____ : _____   _____

After-School

_____
_____
_____
_____
_____
_____
_____
_____
_____
_____
_____
_____
_____
_____
_____
_____
_____
_____
_____
_____
_____
_____
_____
_____
_____

Weekly Goals :

_____
_____
_____

Chores / Daily To-Do's :   M T W TH F S S

_____   ◯ ◯ ◯ ◯ ◯ ◯ ◯
_____   ◯ ◯ ◯ ◯ ◯ ◯ ◯
_____   ◯ ◯ ◯ ◯ ◯ ◯ ◯
_____   ◯ ◯ ◯ ◯ ◯ ◯ ◯
_____   ◯ ◯ ◯ ◯ ◯ ◯ ◯

Notes :

―――――――――――――――――― Weekend Plans ――

Saturday   Sunday

_____   _____
_____   _____
_____   _____
_____   _____

Monday   /   School

_____ : _____   _____
_____ : _____   _____
_____ : _____   _____
_____ : _____   _____
_____ : _____   _____

Tuesday   /

_____ : _____   _____
_____ : _____   _____
_____ : _____   _____
_____ : _____   _____
_____ : _____   _____

Wednesday   /

_____ : _____   _____
_____ : _____   _____
_____ : _____   _____
_____ : _____   _____
_____ : _____   _____

Thursday   /

_____ : _____   _____
_____ : _____   _____
_____ : _____   _____
_____ : _____   _____

Friday   /

_____ : _____   _____
_____ : _____   _____
_____ : _____   _____
_____ : _____   _____
_____ : _____   _____

After-School

_____
_____
_____
_____
_____
_____
_____
_____
_____
_____
_____
_____
_____
_____
_____
_____
_____
_____
_____
_____
_____
_____
_____
_____
_____

Weekly Goals :

_____
_____
_____

Chores / Daily To-Do's :   M T W TH F S S

_____   ◯ ◯ ◯ ◯ ◯ ◯ ◯
_____   ◯ ◯ ◯ ◯ ◯ ◯ ◯
_____   ◯ ◯ ◯ ◯ ◯ ◯ ◯
_____   ◯ ◯ ◯ ◯ ◯ ◯ ◯
_____   ◯ ◯ ◯ ◯ ◯ ◯ ◯

Notes :

Weekend Plans

Saturday   Sunday

_____   _____
_____   _____
_____   _____
_____   _____
_____   _____

KAHOOTIE CO.

Monday   /   *School*

_____ : _____   _____
_____ : _____   _____
_____ : _____   _____
_____ : _____   _____
_____ : _____   _____

Tuesday   /

_____ : _____   _____
_____ : _____   _____
_____ : _____   _____
_____ : _____   _____

Wednesday   /

_____ : _____   _____
_____ : _____   _____
_____ : _____   _____
_____ : _____   _____

Thursday   /

_____ : _____   _____
_____ : _____   _____
_____ : _____   _____
_____ : _____   _____
_____ : _____   _____

Friday   /

_____ : _____   _____
_____ : _____   _____
_____ : _____   _____
_____ : _____   _____

After-School

_____
_____
_____
_____
_____
_____
_____
_____
_____
_____
_____
_____
_____
_____
_____
_____
_____
_____
_____
_____
_____
_____
_____
_____

Weekly Goals :

_____
_____
_____

Chores / Daily To-Do's :   M T W TH F S S

_____   ○ ○ ○ ○ ○ ○ ○
_____   ○ ○ ○ ○ ○ ○ ○
_____   ○ ○ ○ ○ ○ ○ ○
_____   ○ ○ ○ ○ ○ ○ ○
_____   ○ ○ ○ ○ ○ ○ ○

Notes :

Weekend Plans

Saturday   Sunday

_____   _____
_____   _____
_____   _____
_____   _____
_____   _____

Monday / School

_____ : _____   _____
_____ : _____   _____
_____ : _____   _____
_____ : _____   _____
_____ : _____   _____

Tuesday /

_____ : _____   _____
_____ : _____   _____
_____ : _____   _____
_____ : _____   _____

Wednesday /

_____ : _____   _____
_____ : _____   _____
_____ : _____   _____
_____ : _____   _____
_____ : _____   _____

Thursday /

_____ : _____   _____
_____ : _____   _____
_____ : _____   _____
_____ : _____   _____

Friday /

_____ : _____   _____
_____ : _____   _____
_____ : _____   _____
_____ : _____   _____
_____ : _____   _____

After-School

_____
_____
_____
_____
_____

_____
_____
_____
_____
_____

_____
_____
_____
_____
_____

_____
_____
_____
_____
_____

_____
_____
_____
_____

Weekly Goals :

_____
_____
_____

Chores / Daily To-Do's : M T W TH F S S

_____ ○ ○ ○ ○ ○ ○ ○

_____ ○ ○ ○ ○ ○ ○ ○

_____ ○ ○ ○ ○ ○ ○ ○

_____ ○ ○ ○ ○ ○ ○ ○

_____ ○ ○ ○ ○ ○ ○ ○

Notes :

Weekend Plans

Saturday   Sunday

_____   _____

_____   _____

_____   _____

_____   _____

Monday   /   *School*

_____ : _____   _____
_____ : _____   _____
_____ : _____   _____
_____ : _____   _____
_____ : _____   _____

Tuesday   /

_____ : _____   _____
_____ : _____   _____
_____ : _____   _____
_____ : _____   _____
_____ : _____   _____

Wednesday   /

_____ : _____   _____
_____ : _____   _____
_____ : _____   _____
_____ : _____   _____
_____ : _____   _____

Thursday   /

_____ : _____   _____
_____ : _____   _____
_____ : _____   _____
_____ : _____   _____
_____ : _____   _____

Friday   /

_____ : _____   _____
_____ : _____   _____
_____ : _____   _____
_____ : _____   _____
_____ : _____   _____

After-School

_____
_____
_____
_____
_____
_____
_____
_____
_____
_____
_____
_____
_____
_____
_____
_____
_____
_____
_____
_____
_____
_____
_____

Weekly Goals :

_____
_____
_____

Chores / Daily To-Do's :   M T W TH F S S

_____   ◯ ◯ ◯ ◯ ◯ ◯ ◯
_____   ◯ ◯ ◯ ◯ ◯ ◯ ◯
_____   ◯ ◯ ◯ ◯ ◯ ◯ ◯
_____   ◯ ◯ ◯ ◯ ◯ ◯ ◯
_____   ◯ ◯ ◯ ◯ ◯ ◯ ◯

Notes :

Weekend Plans

Saturday   Sunday

_____   _____
_____   _____
_____   _____
_____   _____
_____   _____

KAHOOTIE CO.

_____ : _____   _____

_____ : _____   _____

_____ : _____   _____

_____ : _____   _____

_____ : _____   _____

Tuesday   /

_____ : _____   _____

_____ : _____   _____

_____ : _____   _____

_____ : _____   _____

_____ : _____   _____

Wednesday   /

_____ : _____   _____

_____ : _____   _____

_____ : _____   _____

_____ : _____   _____

_____ : _____   _____

Thursday   /

_____ : _____   _____

_____ : _____   _____

_____ : _____   _____

_____ : _____   _____

_____ : _____   _____

Friday   /

_____ : _____   _____

_____ : _____   _____

_____ : _____   _____

_____ : _____   _____

_____ : _____   _____

After-School

Weekly Goals :

Chores / Daily To-Do's : M T W TH F S S

Notes :

Weekend Plans

Saturday   Sunday

Monday   /   *School*

_____ : _____   _____

_____ : _____   _____

_____ : _____   _____

_____ : _____   _____

_____ : _____   _____

Tuesday   /

_____ : _____   _____

_____ : _____   _____

_____ : _____   _____

_____ : _____   _____

_____ : _____   _____

Wednesday   /

_____ : _____   _____

_____ : _____   _____

_____ : _____   _____

_____ : _____   _____

_____ : _____   _____

Thursday   /

_____ : _____   _____

_____ : _____   _____

_____ : _____   _____

_____ : _____   _____

Friday   /

_____ : _____   _____

_____ : _____   _____

_____ : _____   _____

_____ : _____   _____

After-School

_____
_____
_____
_____
_____
_____
_____
_____
_____
_____
_____
_____
_____
_____
_____
_____
_____
_____
_____
_____

Weekly Goals :

_____
_____
_____

Chores / Daily To-Do's :

	M	T	W	TH	F	S	S
_____	◯	◯	◯	◯	◯	◯	◯
_____	◯	◯	◯	◯	◯	◯	◯
_____	◯	◯	◯	◯	◯	◯	◯
_____	◯	◯	◯	◯	◯	◯	◯
_____	◯	◯	◯	◯	◯	◯	◯

Notes :

Weekend Plans

Saturday	Sunday
_____	_____
_____	_____
_____	_____
_____	_____
_____	_____

Made in the USA
Middletown, DE
04 May 2022

65279861R00073